Just Like Claire

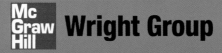

Mc Graw Hill **Wright Group**

Louis watched his sister eat.
His stomach **growled**.

grrr!

When Claire got up,
Louis ran to the table.
He ate rice and beans
just like Claire.

Louis watched his sister read.

When Claire went out to play,
Louis picked up the book.
He read about stars
just like Claire.

Louis watched his sister
play soccer.

Claire tried to **bounce** the ball
into the goal.
The ball missed.

"Move your knees quickly,"
someone said.

It was their brother, Marcel!

"Louis, do you want to try?"
Marcel asked.

Louis ran down to them.

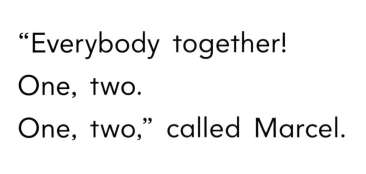

"Everybody together!
One, two.
One, two," called Marcel.

Louis moved his knees
just like Claire.
Claire moved her knees
just like Marcel.

Focus Question

How is my family a part of who I am?

Act out a scene in the book.

My Home Page